The N

Frank McGuinness was bc ....ana, Co. Donegal, and now lives in Dublin and lectures in English at University College Dublin. His plays include: *The Factory Girls* (Abbey Theatre, Dublin, 1982), *Baglady* (Abbey, 1985), *Observe the Sons of Ulster Marching Towards the Somme* (Abbey, 1985; Hampstead Theatre, London, 1986), *Innocence* (Gate Theatre, Dublin, 1986), *Carthaginians* (Abbey, 1988; Hampstead, 1989), *Mary and Lizzie* (RSC, 1989), *The Bread Man* (Gate, 1991), *Someone Who'll Watch Over Me* (Hampstead, West End and Broadway, 1992), *The Bird Sanctuary* (Abbey, 1994), *Mutabilitie* (NT, 1997), *Dolly West's Kitchen* (Abbey, 1999; Old Vic, 2000), *Gates of Gold* (Gate, 2002), *Speaking Like Magpies* (Swan, Stratford, 2005), *There Came a Gypsy Riding* (Almeida, London, 2007) and *Greta Garbo Came to Donegal* (Tricycle, 2010). His widely performed versions include *Rosmersholm* (1987), *Yerma* (1987), *Peer Gynt* (1988), *Three Sisters* (1990), *The Threepenny Opera* (1991), *Hedda Gabler* (1994), *Uncle Vanya* (1995), *A Doll's House* (1997), *The Caucasian Chalk Circle* (1997), *Electra* (1998), *The Storm* (1998), *Miss Julie* (2000), *Hecuba* (2004), *Phaedra* (2006), *The Lady from the Sea* (2008), *Oedipus* (2008), *Helen* (2009), *Ghosts* (2010) and *John Gabriel Borkman* (2010).

also by Frank McGuinness

FRANK McGUINNESS

The Match Box

ff

faber and faber

First published in 2012
by Faber and Faber Limited
74–77 Great Russell Street
London WC1B 3DA

Typeset by Country Setting, Kingsdown, Kent CT14 8ES
Printed in England by CPI Group (UK) Ltd, Croydon, CRO 4YY

A CIP record for this book
is available from the British Library

978-0-571-29742-9

2 4 6 8 10 9 7 5 3 1

For Sorcha Cusack

The Match Box was produced by Liverpool Everyman and Playhouse and first performed at the Playhouse Theatre Studio on 14 June 2012.

Sal Leanne Best

Director Lia Williams
Designer Colin Richmond
Lighting Designer Charlie Lucas
Sound and Composition Giles Perring
Recorded voices Esme Herbert and Melanie Pappenheim

Character

Sal
an English woman of Irish descent

Place
Valentia Island,
off the coast of County Kerry

Time
The present

THE MATCH BOX

Sal is dressed for a summer's day.
As the play progresses, light softly fades
as morning moves through afternoon
into evening and early night.

The music is of the production's own choosing.

Sal It is quiet. So quiet you can hear yourself breathe. A peaceful place, this island. If you had told me years ago – when I was a young girl – this would be where I'd end my days – spend my days I meant to say – if you had told me that, I would have thought you were cracked. Lovely to come here for holidays, see what relations are still living, do the social duties, and then run wild like a billygoat, wild for the rest of the summer. You come here looking like a lady, my Aunt Breda would say – a fine lady from England with a lovely accent – and within a week you're already a savage like the rest of them.

They're nearly all gone now. My aunts and uncles, dead and buried. The island's growing deserted. What few cousins are still here, they cross the bridge to work in the mainland. The school closed a few years ago. What kids remain, they get the bus into the town. No sound of children at all during the day. That's part of the reason for the silence. Quite eerie at times. Something absent. Not that anybody mentions children to me. Say nothing out of respect. Or maybe it's fear. They're a superstitious people.

That's why they were quite glad when I showed my face occasionally at Mass. Heathen England hadn't hardened me entirely. I still had time for the old faith. One or two of the neighbours even hinted it might have been a source of comfort. The look in my face put a stop to that gallop. I don't mind their sympathy. That I would expect. But I won't take that nonsense about comfort. What happened,

happened. I live with it as best I can. I keep myself to myself on that subject, thank you very much. I have nothing further to add or to hide, I assure you. I said what I had to say about forgiveness, and much good it did me. Still to a man and to a woman, they'd each say about me, she's bearing up, she's not bitter, considering – considering –

She strikes a match and watches it burn.

There is I find something pleasant about the smell of sulphur. I always have done. These give off quite a tang.

She rattles the matches in the box.

She reads its name.

'Maguire and Paterson – established 1882. Cara Safety Matches.' I had a pal in school – she was called Cara. A sweet girl, bit nervy. She believed in fate. She said that to me – we were about nine years old. I'd never heard the word fate before, but Cara announced to all and sundry she believed in it, and she smiled when she declared this, because her fate in life, she maintained, was to be kind to everyone – in the Irish language, you see, Cara meant friend, she explained. That's what she tried to be. And it's true – everyone liked her. Then she went away. We had a party for her – well, her parents did. And here's the funny thing. Not everyone showed up.

Very few did, in fact. She was beside herself, Cara. She couldn't believe it. She'd delivered the invites personally. Couldn't blame the post. Where were they all? She locked herself in her bedroom. Wouldn't show her face. We could hear her sobbing. The few of us there, we just sat downstairs, really embarrassed, making up something – anything to say. And Cara's mum – she was so angry. Now I think she must have started to hit the bottle. Her

4

dad too, he was in a right tizzy, shouting for Cara to be with her mates, not stuck as usual in her bloody den.

That was when her mother turned on us, demanding to know where were the other bitches? They had let her daughter down, and why had they done it? We couldn't tell her, so she ordered us out, and we legged it, willingly. She was crazed now. She shouted after us – good riddance to bad rubbish, you pack of fuckers. And we were shocked. So shocked. We were little girls. No one had ever called us such a name before. No one used words like that in our company. And we never saw Cara again. Never heard a word from her, wherever she disappeared to – which wasn't a surprise. Within a week no one missed her. All we could remember was her lunatic drunkard of a mother screaming curses after us. So much for being kind to everyone – for being a friend. Cara.

She looks again at the match box and reads.

'Safety matches' – what does that mean? That they don't burn you?

She strikes a match and lets it burn.

It went out by itself. That must be it. It's set alight. It glows. It goes out. There is a fixed time for it to flare. After that, it's gone. Maybe the way you strike it – that decides how long it lasts. Maybe it's the way you hold it, the angle – the distance from yourself – the nearer to you, the shorter time it burns. If you were to get a stopwatch, the most precise stopwatch in the world, like something you see used in the Olympic Games, one that measures down to a thousand of a second, if you were to use that, you'd discover no two matches ever lasted the exact amount of time. Each one was different – each has its own span of life and then it was exhausted, extinguished, burnt itself out, falling from your hand, having served its purpose, its job done – the cigarette lit, the Zip lighters blazing in the grate, warming the whole house, the screams from the coal, from the wood, burning . . . burning . . . burning . . .

Music.

EPISODE TWO

Sal These are the things you start wondering – how long each match lasts – when you live in a place where you can hear yourself breathing. It does affect you, when you're not that used to it, living away from a crowd of people. It's beyond question things sound different. For instance the fields – the green fields, I swear they have their own way of talking. You might be passing by one and it starts calling your name in a way you'd never imagine. You have to resist the temptation to stand still and listen or else you'd get nothing done. And it's not just the land has a language here. I swear this is true, I was passing by a flock of sheep and lambs and I could hear them whisper, don't kill me, don't eat me. Strange, very strange, but as I say, true as I'm standing here. I answered the lambs, and I said, why have you started to talk to me? They said you know damned well why – it's because of your daughter. And I wondered how did they know her? How did they know me? But that's when they chose to ignore me and go back to chewing the grass, as if nothing untoward had happened, as if the animals had not begun to accuse me – accuse me of what, I can't say, but I know when it's happening, because I've faced my fair share in my time, let me tell you.

There was consternation before she was born. My mother – I thought she'd blow a gasket. From the day and hour I hit my teens she was expecting trouble. She let me know it. My dad was the steady one. Always calming her down. Pouring her a large whiskey or a big glass of red wine. Get that into you – there is nothing a slow drink won't solve. His remedy for all ills. This time

7

it didn't cure him of his own panic. His darling girl up the spout, and with no intention of telling who was the baker of her bun in the oven. It was the nearest he ever came to raising his hand against me. Part of me wished he would. Knock me into the middle of next week – next month – next year – when this bump would be born and we'll all be back to normal. Yet it was anything but normal. It was my dad who was crying – not speaking, not saying anything. When he did speak, it was to lose his temper completely. And herself – my mother – as always she was the one you could not – could never predict. No, she was a rock, and one word did not borrow another, she was minding my father more than she was me, almost as if she didn't care.

She did though. She made that clear when she took me aside for a private conversation. Woman to woman, she whispered. Are you keeping this baby or are you not? If you're not, I want you to know I'll back you in that as much as I will if you do have the child. That was her first comment. I knew from her voice that she meant exactly what she said – my Irish Catholic maniac of a mother. I was in such a state of shock I nodded. That was all I could do. Do you want to have the infant adopted? I shook my head. Then you'll rear it yourself – is that what you want? I said it was. Did I want to stay in England when I was expecting? What did she mean? Would I like to go to Ireland – to Kerry – and be with the family there? Why would I want that? Do you not want your baby to be Irish? she asked me. And I burst out laughing. I thought that was the funniest thing in the world. What did it matter for Christ's sake if the child was from Timbuctoo? What a stupid thing to ask. And as I said that I watched her wince. No, not wince – it was as if she cowered, as if I hit her. As if she was sharing something about herself with me for the first time, and

8

I thought it was stupid. What a cruel cow I was. And I knew it. And I knew what to call my daughter when I first set eyes on her. She would be Mary – for my mother.

She lights a match and lets it burn but does not let it fall, holding the charred remains in the palm of her hand.

Anyone seeing their baby after it's been born, we all think they are the image of our parents, my mother, my father, her mother, his father, their mothers and fathers, stretching all the way back to Adam and Eve, until I picture them in Eden, playing with Cain and Abel, arguing over which resembles the other more closely, inventing for themselves a history God himself could not create, for this is all our doing, this is our humanity, and let no divine being dare claim he made us – we made the world, we made ourselves. I saw every life before me, every death behind me, in the face of my infant. And she grew to be a girl, my daughter, my Mary. Sing a song, Mary. Sing for Grandma and Granda. Sing.

She sings lowly.

Mary had a little lamb
Its fleece was white as snow
And everywhere that Mary went
The lamb was sure to go

It followed her to school one day
That was against the rules –

That was against the rules.

She stops singing, and lets the charred remains of the burnt match in her palm fall.

She speaks.

9

It made the children laugh and play
To see a lamb at school.

She stops speaking and there is a brief silence she soon interrupts.

And I did go back to school after she was born. They insisted. My dad did. My mum didn't disagree. That was it. Go to college. Study. Get a decent job. Support yourself. Support the two of you. And I did. Two jobs if I had to. Three, if there were enough hours in the day. But there weren't. Still and all, we did not want. I think that's fair to say. We did not want. For I had her, she had me – no need of a man, no need of a car. Slog your guts out in an office. Do a few hours in Waitrose. Save for Christmas. For the holidays. I combed her hair like it was gold. Precious. On her soft head. Her as quiet as my father. Thinking, planning, knowing something – Jesus, do you think she knew?

She rapidly strikes another match and lets it fall burning.

You see – that's what happens when you hear things speaking.

It was this bloody box –

She rattles the match box.

That's what put this madness in my mind. And it is mad to think like that. How in hell could she know? And if she did want to know anything, she'd ask. I always told her – ask me. If I can answer, I will. So who's my father? – how come you have not told me that? – how come I don't know who's my dad? Are you ever going to tell me?

Silence.

I didn't. Never did. Didn't want him in our lives. He had no right to have anything to do with us – her nor me. But by God she was a stubborn child, stubborn as I was, refusing to take no for an answer, asking till she was blue in the face. She did not get the better of me. How can I tell her he was the man who fucked and legged it, the loser who took one look at my belly, my big belly, and burst out laughing, roaring – if you ever say that brat is mine I'll kill it, and I'll kill you. Charming, as they say. A fine specimen of manhood. Yes, I was never going to name him when she put me under cross-examination. And she never believed me – I know that. She never believed me when I finally said the shit didn't want to know. He turned his back and never lifted a finger. Your father didn't want us. Better you hear that sooner rather than later. Accept it. For God's sake, you can't have everything. You have me – stop asking for him – he's not there. But she never did stop asking. Well, she never stopped wondering. And he did show up – after the funeral – his heart broken.

Silence.

His heart was broken – he said.

Silence.

I did not open the door to him. What grief was it of his? I can hear him, crying in pubs, confessing all his sins. Sins of neglect, sins of omission, and the greatest sin of all – what is the greatest sin of all? Being too late – too fucking late, and he was always that. So I left him standing outside, with his straggly beard and black overcoat, weeping his eyes out for the child he never knew. Did he know what she liked for breakfast? Did he see her on her first day at school? You wouldn't let me – that was his defence – you'd never let me – that's what he was calling. Did he listen when she lost her temper if she didn't get her own way? I wasn't allowed near her, he was shouting. And I shouted back there are ways – legal ways to have got near her, but you did not bother, you don't know how much that young lady had to be the boss. What colour she'd wear – what drink she'd like – how many – precisely how many cornflakes she'd eat – what time she would deign to go to bed. No, you knew nothing about – nothing – nothing – nothing. I was now hoarse shouting at him. Foolish woman, what was the point? He'd already done what he was best doing – he'd vanished. But I still called after him did he know the slightest detail about the biggest fight of all – the battle of will I'd vowed I'd win – and it was all over a rabbit.

I want a rabbit, she declared. I can't afford a rabbit, I lied. She knew every time I wasn't telling the truth. I want a rabbit – a black rabbit. You have a hamster. The hamster is boring – he doesn't do anything. And what's the ruddy rabbit going to do? Sing in the choir – dress up – play rock scissors paper? I don't care – I want a rabbit. You're not getting one – they stink the house out. I want a rabbit. You have a hamster. But she didn't for much longer. The hamster popped his clogs – or his paws – or whatever hamsters do.

And there was great weeping and gnashing of teeth from Madam. In fact there was a bit too much weeping. That child is inconsolable, the girls at work, Janet and Big Sophie, decided. They knew all about the rabbit demand – they were on her side as well. Big Sophie declared it was the saddest thing in the world for a kid to lose her pet. She should know – she'd never recovered from the disappearance of her mongoose. Your what? Janet asked her, you had a mongoose? She did, yes, its name was Millicent, her dad bought her. Anyway, Millicent disappeared – Sophie's mum was suspected but admitted nothing and the rest of the family, their hearts were broken. Buy Mary a rabbit – that was the general consensus. All right, I said. We'll play for it. We did. I was paper. She was scissors. She won. We knew the deal. So muggins here did as she was told.

This bloody rabbit was the ugliest bastard you'd ever set eyes on. There were nice fluffy little white ones, sleeping in their cages, and one bruiser who looked as if he could line up for Hull Kingston Rovers. I swear to God I saw a look in his eye that threatened me if I didn't take him home, he knew where we lived and he'd follow us and burn the house to the ground. I still asked her was she sure? She said she was. Why him – why not one of the baby ones? They're the same size as my hamster was. They make me sad. I want something different. So we got something different, and his name was Terence.

As I am in my way a mother of some sort to Terence, I do not like to speak ill of the creature, but if you were to put a gun to my head and demand I say something nice, all I could honestly observe by way of compliment is that he had an uncanny knack for crapping. Crapping in the most unusual places. Crapping in nooks and crannies of our house I never knew existed, let alone smelt. I did not blame my daughter nor did I blame Terence for his almighty capacity to evacuate his bowels. No, I reserved my censure for a certain individual passing under the name of Big Sophie. Why me? she squealed, how am I responsible? The touching story of Millicent the mongoose swung me – that's when I decided to buy Mary a rabbit. Did you believe that yarn about a mongoose? she asked, God, it's years since I spun that one. Where in hell would we get our hands on a bloody mongoose? You're the right one – fall for anything. I didn't start crying over an ostrich called Oona – spelt with two 'o's, did I? she asked. No, you didn't, I snarled. Oh good, she said, then I hadn't gone on the gin and got completely out of it. I just make these things up when I've had a few. Quite sweet and childlike, isn't it?

I gave her my reply. My reply was not sweet and childlike. She looked quite offended, but Janet bought us both a coffee and we shared a doughnut at break time, so harmony was restored. And the rabbit – Terence – became part of the family – part of the furniture it so frequently shat on. He was a biter. Even went for Mary sometimes. We were all a bit afraid of it, except my mother. Try anything on and she'd let a fist fall on its skull, sending it spinning. Put manners on the blighter, she declared. And Terence respected her. And Mary loved him. Yes, she did. Where is it now? Alive, I hope. Free, anyway, as I've said. Yes, I set it free – one of the first things I remember doing after the news. Thought of offering it to Sophie, or to Janet, but I couldn't. Sophie would have said no, but Janet – maybe she might have wanted it. Who knows? Too late now. It was her who broke the bad word first to me – Janet.

She goes to light a match, hesitates, then strikes it and lets it fall.

Music.

Sal Well, Janet tried to tell me, God love her. She did try, but me – I couldn't hear. I couldn't listen to what she was saying. I just caught the words policeman and policewoman. I couldn't make out anything else. Because she was starting to cry, Janet. And Sophie, there she was beside Janet, and the two of them, they were the colour of a ghost. The boss, Mr Jackson, he was there as well – holding my hand, asking me would he phone my next of kin? What has next of kin got to do with anything? Am I dead or something? Sal, you're not listening to us, Janet said. Do you not hear what you've just been told? And I suppose I hadn't. How can I bloody hear what Sophie is blubbing there? How can anyone hear anything? You're in a state of shock, Mr Jackson kept repeating, she is in a state of shock. Will someone phone the next of kin? He's off again about next of kin. What is wrong with this man? What is wrong with the lot of you? Tell me out straight. Sophie, she caught me – she held me in her arms – she said the police are here. They want to talk to you. It's about Mary. She's been killed. Killed dead.

Silence.

Dead.

Silence.

Dead. And do you know what was the first thing I did? I looked at my watch. I said, have I the right time? Is it quarter to four? Nobody answered. They just gave me a funny look. Has the cat got your tongues? Is it quarter to four? Because if it is, Mary's at home by now. School finishes at three. She walks with her pals to the minder.

Has a snack there – does a bit of her homework – I collect her at five or thereabouts – drive to the house – and we catch up on the day. That's life. That's our life. So what the hell are you talking about, killed dead? What's got into you?

It's not us, Janet said, it's the police. They want to talk to you. I'm sorry, I have nothing to do with the police. It will be her father – that's who they're looking for. Not my business. I won't meet them. You have to meet them, Sal – it is your business, and Sophie was now not going to take no for an answer.

That's when they came in. A bloke about forty, a girl – younger than me. Wearing uniforms. And they had the cheek to tell me some lie. Mary was dead. She'd been shot in the street. Caught in crossfire. Gangs firing at each other. Innocent victim. Palaver – pure palaver, not a word of truth in it. I did, however, hear them out civilly. Manners were instilled into me by my parents, and I pride myself I did the same with my flesh and blood, but it was all I could do to restrain myself when I wanted to lash out at the pair of them for coming to a woman's place of work and spreading such a cruel story in front of all and sundry. Had they nothing better to do with their time?

I played along with their little game. I nodded politely. I thanked them very much for their concern. I did appreciate it terribly, but I think if they were to make further inquiries they would discover they were mistaken and could they please take themselves elsewhere? My daughter was hale and hearty and waiting for me to collect her as usual. She isn't, Sal, the policewoman said to me, she isn't waiting. Then what have you done with her? Where have you hidden her? Do we even know if you're what you say you are? Maybe you've abducted her. Maybe you're not even the police. Have you shown us identification? Why should we believe you? Remember, Sophie – your birthday, the male stripper – he was dressed as a copper – are you going to throw all your clothes off and tell me this is a great joke? Have you put them up to this, Sophie? Well, I can tell you I don't find this at all amusing. I like a laugh as much as the next, but you've gone too far. That's when I heard Sophie screaming – for Christ's sake, it's not a joke, it's really happening, will you listen? And then she did something very strange. She just collapsed in the boss's arms – no love lost ever between those two – but she just started to weep, saying she was sorry, so sorry, so very sorry.

What can you do when someone is that genuinely upset? I put my hands around her fat face, all red with tears. I said, it's all right, love – it's all right, I'm not angry. Don't be punishing yourself like this. You've played a trick on me. You've taken it too far, but we can stop now. I'm going to forgive you, so stop this crying. And I knew everything was going to be fine because out of the blue I swear she started laughing, and so too did I – I was laughing at the whole escapade. That's when I saw my mother and father coming into the room. And they weren't – they weren't laughing.

She lights another match and lets it fall.

Music.

EPISODE FOUR

Sal There had to be a formal identification of the body, preferably by a blood relation. My father, he offered to do the necessary. My mother said she would go with him. It was very brave of them. Mam kept repeating we just want to get her home – lay our hands on whoever did this and lock them away for life. She pointed her finger at me. She said, look at the state of my girl. She hasn't even taken it in yet. She doesn't know what's happened. She'll never recover. But she was wrong there. I had taken it in. I did know what happened.

I thanked my parents for their kindness in sparing me the shock of going through seeing my child dead in a morgue, but I could not possibly accept they do the identifying. I felt that was my task – my responsibility. To a man and to a woman they tried to talk me out of it. It would kill me stone dead. That shock on top of all the other shocks – too much for any mother. Spare yourself that sight for the love of God. No avail. I would do as I'd decided. I'd see my daughter myself. And all the while that expression, for the love of God, that was ringing in my ears. I would not exactly say it was a comfort to me. No, not a comfort, but I did think to myself it could be useful. And that's what kept the legs beneath me from bending. I must look out and remember whatever I can salvage from all this and use it now or later to my advantage, for this was not an end but a beginning.

Still and all, it seemed like an ending when I set eyes on her. I did want to go alone. In fact, I was insisting on that. But they just wouldn't hear of it. Maybe I was expected to faint, and a safe pair of hands was needed to catch the distraught mother. Sadly, I could not oblige with that particular melodramatic touch, but I have to admit that I thought my father was going to pass out at the sight in front of us.

It wasn't as if the body was mauled by wild animals or smashed into smithereens or stabbed to ribbons. Nothing quite like that, but it was pretty clear how shocked the poor fellow was. Is that her? I heard him asking, and my mother, she snapped back, who the hell do you think it is? But I could understand how he doubted what he was seeing. My daughter, Mary, was twelve years old – but lying there, on that cold slab, she could have been seventy. She was like an old lady, not like a child, not like Mary who set out for school that morning. Or was it the day after she died, we saw her stretched out there? The week after, even – I can't remember but I do remember when I reached out to touch her I was really surprised at how warm she felt. Yes, it's her – it's definitely her, I heard myself saying, but do you really still think she's dead, because she's not cold – she's not really cold, is she, Mum? Just feel the heat of her.

My mum took my hand and said, Sal, that's the warmth of your own body, not hers. Is she definitely not breathing? Are you sure, Mum, she's not breathing? Her lips are dry, aren't they? Did anyone bring water? Will I wet her lips with water? Did anyone think of that? I bend down to listen to her mouth, but it was silent. Not a syllable – not a sound out of it. I knew that somewhere inside her – outside her – all through her – all around her – I knew there must be a hole that the bullet made going through her. I couldn't see it, but I could feel it, for there was something similar inside me. There was a hole and it was not in my heart. No, that hole, it was my heart.

She does not weep but strikes a match, letting it fall.

She strikes another match, letting it fall.

My heart.

She strikes another match and lets it fall.

My heart.

Silence.

By this stage my mum and dad were in floods of tears, but my eyes – they were bone dry. And that's how they are going to stay. Let the rest of them bawl their fill. But that is not going to be my way. I have other things to do. Mind my folks, for a start, because I do believe – I really do believe one of them is going to die as well. I don't know which, but I do know I've never thought of them as old people until that day. Now I can see every drink they've ever downed – every cigarette they've ever smoked – every feed of fat and grease – every sleep they've ever missed – every kick life's given them in the face – I can see signs of all that when I look at them. And it hits me like a fist in the stomach they will be taken from me as well. Of course I've always known that in some way this must happen but now it's like that's been hammered into my head, and that is when I think I'm going to crack. I'm going to explode. My eyes are going to burst. But I look away from them and concentrate on the child, stretched out cold before me.

And this is the strangest thing of all. I can hear her voice speaking to me. No one else can. I'm sure of that because then they would stop bawling. And I have to find out what it is she is whispering to me. The first thing I can make out is, don't cry – don't cry, Mum. Don't. So I don't. But I also knew this is not the time to ask her out loud and straight then what is it I should do?

For if I speak to her, the world will think me mad and
I am, despite all intends and purposes, I am in command.
The proof of that is I keep my counsel. I do not panic.
I do not start shouting – she is speaking, my dead child
is talking. No, I am restrained. I have patience. I can
wait till I'm on my own. But I'm not left on my own,
am I?

Music.

Sal The world wants to comfort me. The world wants me to make a comment. The world won't leave me alone. And what I want is to be left alone, so I best accept their comfort and I will make a comment, but no, no – I don't need advice on what to wear in front of the cameras, I don't need my solicitors or the police to write out what I should say. I don't want my parents to show their distress at losing their only grandchild by sitting behind me on the screen. I need to say nothing more than what has to be said, and I know what it is going to be, for if I can read between the lines, it's going to be bloody hard to track down the killers and make them cough up to what they've done. That's why they want to write my speech – to hit where it's hardest, they say. But I don't need them to do that for me. I can manage easily myself – just as well, considering what I'm told.

The word is out they'll never find who did it. There is honour among thieves. Isn't that a quaint expression? Where did I drag that from? And they weren't exactly thieves, were they? What did they steal? My peace, my comfort, my hope, my flesh, my daughter. That qualifies as a theft, I suppose. They did commit murder. They did kill. They did leave my child shattered by their bullet. They did cut me and my life to ribbons – cut me to the bone and left me out to die as well. And why did they do it? Because they could. Because they believe they'll get away with it. Because, to them, this is just a joke – bang bang, and when it's over, jump up again. To them nothing has happened – the lot of them. To the police, this is only something that's happened before. This time it's a little girl who's bit the dust. Maybe that will get someone singing, but they doubt it because the murderous bastards who pulled the trigger have everyone too scared to do anything. Not me. I will go amongst my enemy and do unto them as they have done to many – as I would do with pleasure unto them.

Or so I think – until I start to see them – imagine her killers. They appear to me as babes in arms, and they are crying, crying for me to feed them. If this came to me in a dream, I think I could manage it. At least, I could explain it. But no, it comes in broad daylight, it comes when I'm sitting still taking in what's been done. It comes when I realise she won't be coming home. She won't be going to school. She won't be having sleepovers with her mates. It comes to me when I say the words, Mary is dead, isn't she? And Sophie, she answers me, yes, Sal, she is, love, she is dead.

Silence.

What is it that brings them to me like that? Why do they come to me, helpless in their mothers' arms? Why do their mothers have the faces of wolves? They open their mouths to kiss their children, and all that comes out are howls of hatred. Hated the day and hour they came from the womb. Conceived in hatred, carried in hatred, born in hatred, reared in hatred, and now spreading the disease of their hatred, infecting anything that comes in the way – they who were poisoned by their mother's milk. Survived it and spewed it in the faces of any unfortunate enough to cross their path, unfortunate like my innocent daughter. I know what should have been done to them. Put down at birth. And it's not too late to do that. Put them down. One at a time or all together.

I'm not choosy. And when I've settled on doing that –
when my head is clear as a bell – they come back to me
as babies – infants – little boys bawling for attention
nobody gave them. And now, will I not either?

She lights a match and lets it fall.

Sal I wish you would let me at least see an outline of what you plan to read out at the press conference – my solicitor, Peter, he's getting quite worried. That's why he's pestering me. The television won't allow it to go out live until they're given a copy. The police are strongly advising you to let them have a look.

I shake my head. All I reply is, I will have my say and no one will stop me. What have they to be worried about? Am I going to pull out a gun and shoot myself? I don't care if it goes out live. No one is going to dictate to me what I say about my daughter. Is that clear? If it is not acceptable, then I will just be off. The policewoman – what was her name, ah yes, Pearl – Christ, when was the last time you met anyone called Pearl? She tried to talk me out of being so certain I knew what I was doing. Sal, she explained, I wish to God you'd listen to me – I have been through a few of these press conferences and nothing can prepare you for the shock of the camera – the photographers – the flashlights – the sheer bloody heat. Would you not rehearse it so you can hear what it sounds like? Rehearse? What do you think I am? What do you think I'm doing this for? I'm not looking to sell myself. I don't care what I look like or what I sound like. I just want to say my bit and get it over with. Pearl gave me a look that said on your own head be it. And that's precisely how I felt. On my own head be it. For I knew exactly what I was doing. And I knew it was exactly the right thing. I was obeying my instructions to the letter. And it was herself who had issued them, my dead daughter. Remember I told you I could hear her? Me and me alone? Well, this was proof of that. And here is what I said.

One week today my daughter died. My daughter Mary. She was shot in gunfire. I don't know who did it. Neither do the police. Neither does anyone else, it seems, for absolutely nobody has come forward with any information. So many times before mothers and fathers have appeared on TV begging for information, any information, to assist the police investigating the murder of their children. I've watched them, as you've watched me, and I've listened, as you're listening, and thought to myself, thank God, it is not my child – I am not the mother whose heart is splitting. But I am the mother, and this is my child, and when this is over, when you switch off, I won't be doing that, and I don't know what I'll do – I don't know what I will do to cope. All I do know is that I am going to be different from others who've suffered like this – different in one respect. I am not going to beg for your help. No, I am going to offer help. I am going to be there for whoever – man, woman or child – whoever murdered my daughter. I am here waiting for you, because I have something to tell you. It is that I forgive you. I forgive you for having killed Mary. Whatever you have become in life, this crime was not what you were put on this earth to commit. When you were children, little children, you must have had dreams – plans – to be someone wonderful. To grow up and do great things. You would be brave and beautiful and brilliant. That's what my daughter is – what my daughter was.

Silence.

That is why she asks me to forgive you, because your mothers and your fathers do not send you out to maim and destroy – maim yourselves and destroy your own

26

lives as surely as you have done mine and my family's.
That is why I offer you my sorrow and my sympathy,
because we are now connected for the rest of our
existence. I cannot, I will not forget what you have done,
and neither will you. I said I didn't know what I was
going to do, but I know what you must. Go and tell
what you have done. Admit it. I will be here, waiting for
you. Always here, waiting for you. God forgive you.
God bless you. And I hope He will forgive and bless me
for what I've said about you, and to you. I hope He will
forgive and bless us all. Thank you.

Music.

Sal I think it fair to say all hell broke loose when I
finished speaking. Pearl looked as if I'd slapped her hard.
There was no clapping. No one said, well done. Sophie
just shook her head. And no one came near me. So if hell
is the silentest place you can ever imagine, then yes, I'm
certain it did break loose. It was left up to me to ask,
was it all right? Why is no one speaking? You've just
taken us all aback, Sal – I don't think anyone was
expecting what you came out with. That was from Peter,
the solicitor. What did you want me to say? What should
I have told them? Sophie recovered her voice and said,
you spoke as you found, you couldn't do more than that,
it's just that. And she started to falter. Just that what? I
challenged her. What's with all the God bless and God
forgive? That just doesn't strike me as your style. And
what do you mean you forgive them? That Mary
forgives them? I'm sorry, but I don't follow – I don't
understand. I just don't.

And she wasn't alone. My parents were silent as the
grave. All my mother said was we'd best get you home.
My dad told the taxi driver to drop them off first. His
reaction when we were in the house – it gave me the
fright of my life. He slammed his two fists down on the
kitchen table. Called me a thundering disgrace. What
kind of creature does not mourn her child? Oh Dad,
you've gone too far – that's below the belt. It's meant to
be, he said, what else do you deserve? The dirt that did
this, they must be pissing themselves listening to you,
laughing at the stupid bitch who think she's the Pope –

telling those murderers she forgives them. Get out of my sight, Sal. Get out of this house.

All right, Dad, if that's what you want. And it was. I went to the front door. Opened it. Walked outside. Banged it closed. And I waited. But he didn't rush after me. And where was my mother in all this? She'll have to stick her oar in one way or another. But she left me to stew in my juices. No, in her good time she'll come round.

And she did. Three mornings later. Walked in – very meek and mild. I wasn't going to be the first one to speak. I'd let her start. I was sitting at the table, and there was already a pile of letters I'd opened. Come on, Mum, speak up – ask me what's in these envelopes. She doesn't. Doesn't even sit down. Just looks at me. And shakes her head. I know that gesture. Seen it all my life. She is going to make a pronouncement upon me. That pronouncement will be failure. I have let her down. And this time, as so many times, I have let my father down as well. I am here in mourning for my dead child, still cold in a mortuary and here is this severe lady already engaging in her favourite sport – tearing this fool of a daughter apart at the seams, criticising me without mercy, pushing me into speaking first, asking – as if I need to ask – why are you shaking your head at me?

She opens her mouth, and she stuns me. She says, he believed you, your father. And I've let him. What he doesn't know won't hurt him. And you've done your fair share of that, haven't you? But still and all, I hand it to you. A good show – a very good show – very convincing. Has that taken the wind out of your sails? That I can still see through you entirely? Jesus Christ, do you think you'd fool me? One word of that bloody spiel, do I think you meant it? Think again, lady. I know what you're up to. I know.

And with that she swept the letters from the table. Were people kind enough to send you their sympathy and kindness? To hell with them, she says. A pack of animals did this. That same pack never – ever – inform on each other. That is all you need to know. These letters – I would not clean my arse with them. Neither should you. You well know that. It's in your blood – don't look shocked. That forgiveness – the blessing – all a front. I know what you're capable of doing. And the first step is say nothing.

I said she stunned me. It wasn't just what she had said, but the way she said it. She was not shouting – barely raising her voice. It wasn't as if she was angry even. It was almost like she was beyond anger. She was in control, in complete control, and I would obey her. Don't ask me how – don't ask me when – but I know I would do as my mother told me – my wild savage of a mother, now so strange and calm, so clear and focused – I knew I would do precisely as Mother told me. That is when I noticed she was still standing. All I could reply was sit down, take the weight off your feet, you're making me tired looking at you. She said, yes, you must be tired, Sal. Have you slept at all since you heard the news? No, Mum, I haven't – would you believe I've not been able to go upstairs? I've not set foot in a single room other than this kitchen. Just in case she's hiding somewhere, Mary, and she's going to pop out and give me a nasty shock. But she's not hiding. So I will go up and lie down now.

I went upstairs to go to bed. And I looked in the door where she slept. Where her bedroom was. And I could smell the rabbit. The black rabbit – looking at me. And all her toys. Stuffed toys. Pink and red. Looking at me. I looked back at them. The rabbit – it must have been starving with hunger – but it didn't complain. Not a whimper. Then it hit me. It was waiting. Waiting for Mary to climb the stairs. Come into the room. Take off her clothes. Her socks and her shoes. Get into her pyjamas. Lie on her bed. Fall asleep. The rabbit wanted all that had happened so often before to happen again. Even one more time. But it wasn't going to. Never going to – no, not going to happen. That life was over. Her life was gone. And the rabbit – the black rabbit had lost the girl who loved it. I tried to comfort it, but I couldn't. I couldn't even remember its bloody name. Jesus, am I going bonkers? What is this creature's name? I could no longer bear to look at it. I called out to my mother, get rid of it, please – get it out of my house – find it a home, free it – kill it.

She said she'd do all those things. But first of all I had to do as I'd promised. Grab a bit of sleep. You will be out cold when your head hits the pillow. Even lie down on the top of the sheets in your clothes if you can't face taking them off. No, I need to do that. I need to strip myself naked. I want to see if I'm still there, every part of me, every inch of flesh, every touch of my body. And it was all there – my hands and arms, my feet and hairs, my nose and ears, all there in working order. My mother saw me naked – first time since I was a youngster – and I let her see me to prove to myself I was in the room in the house in the street in the city in the country that was without my daughter. I am without my daughter. I need to go to bed. I need to sleep. You do, my mother said, you do. I slipped beneath the sheets. She tucked me in tight. She asked did I want her to sit with me – sit beside the bed and talk, talk about what we'd do? I said I would be grand on my own. She left me. I fell asleep. And I dreamt of fire. A gigantic fire. Nothing but fire.

She lights a match and lets it fall.

She lights a match and watches it burn.

Music.

Sal We got through the funeral. The world and his wife showed up. I'd laid myself low since the press conference, and we asked for no cameras. That was talking to a brick wall. I knew so few of the mourners. All the kids – her classmates – you'd think I'd have the names of most from all their birthday parties but no – no. They formed a guard of honour at their request. The coffin was carried through it to the hearse. I watched it all, heard the sobbing, dry-eyed. Listened to the priest and to the hymns. Dry-eyed. Bone dry. Went to the grave – the hole in the earth. Dry-eyed. State of shock, I could hear people whispering. Beyond pain. Can't hear us. God knows where her mind is at this day. But Big Sophie, she was worried. In a panic, as a matter of fact. She grabbed me in a hug when it was over and she said, will you cry? If you don't, you will die. I looked at her as if she was mad. A lunatic. A stranger. I waited for her to back away. This was a woman in bad pain, and as the mother of the dead child, I had to do something to sympathise. I said, when you were a little girl, Sophie, did you play I lost my hankie? I lost my handkerchief on my way to school and someone must have found it. Was it you? Was it you? It was you! You drop the hankie and you run, till they catch you. Do you remember? That's what happened to Mary. She lost – what did she lose? Anyway, they caught her, didn't they? And Sophie nodded. She said, yes, they caught her. And now we must catch them, I said. The police, she said, you mean the police? Yes, I said, they will catch them.

Then it was over. Done with. I wonder, did it rain that day? It should have, I suppose. But do you think I could remember? It's strange, but that's what started to happen. I couldn't remember things. Work became a bit of a problem. They were very understanding. And so was I – I understood they couldn't keep me. My father too – he'd never recovered – sinking fast. So that added to my worries. But I really would soon have to knuckle down. Pull myself together. Get a grip. But I didn't. No, I started to go wandering, as they say in Kerry, before or after a death. How's herself coping? She's started wandering – not a good sign. I started to lose track of time. Started to find out what precisely happened to Mary on that day in my own distracted fashion. And the true story did shock me. The story of those murdering boys. Boys I had forgiven, boys I had blessed – what did they do for me?

There were rumours flying. Always rumours flying. They're laughing at the police – the bastards – they're laughing at what they did. They're laughing at me, the fool who asked them to confess to me, tell all and take their punishment. Or their mother, tell their mothers – but here's the kick – they all have only one mother, the three that did it, the three they suspect – they're brothers. A family quarrel. One brother fighting another. Thought he'd reneged to another gang. No chance, so just a family mishap. Not meaning to hit him. Aiming here, there and everywhere. Not caring so long as he missed his brother. Hitting my daughter. Not caring. Playing with guns. Killing my girl. Playing. That's the story – that's what's sweeping through the town. Playing. And they were fucked if they were ever going to inform on who did what. Forget about what they were at each other's throats about then – now it is all hands united, one front against the world. None of the three were near

34

the spot where my daughter died. Each was the other's alibi. And here's the crunch, the sickening one. Their mother – she swears her boys were with her that afternoon. Watching television, drinking a few beers, saving money since one of them is soon to be married. She even sent her commiserations to my good self. She knew what it must be like to lose a kid. Her sons were the light of her life. They were the reason she was put on earth. Like any mother, she would give her life for them. She could not bear the thought of losing a child so violently to death. Her sorrow and sympathy went to any parent in that position. But her boys were innocent. Completely innocent, no matter what was thrown against this family. That was how things were.

She lights a match and watches it burn.

Music.

EPISODE NINE

Sal Funny the things you learn in life – that you pick up just by listening. Did you know if you fire a gun, there's evidence that you did – it goes all over your clothes and your skin? You can burn the clothes to a cinder – the T-shirt and trainers, socks and underpants even, trainers and the laces. Make a big bonfire, watch them turn to ash. But your body – what can you do with that? Here's a handy tip to follow if you ever find yourself in a pickle. What you do is wash yourself. Not with soap and water. That won't do the job. No, you need petrol. Bathe in petrol. Can you imagine the stench? But that will clear you of every stain that proves you are guilty – you did fire the gun. You did the deed. Petrol – can you believe it?

My mother it was who found out that information. She'd been finding out about a lot of things. Those bad boys – they still lived with their mother. Sweet, isn't it? We knew where it was they resided – where they drank – where they worked, occasionally. Don't get me wrong. Mum wasn't so much following them as keeping them at a distance for she said her stomach never could tolerate the smell of shit. Petrol – she said – a little petrol, it absolves them of everything. And my dad said it was a remarkable fluid, useful in more ways than one.

What ways? we asked him. Tell us. He just said rough justice, that's what you get with petrol. We torched a fair few in County Kerry – ones who deserved it. Scald the bastards – blaze them out of house and home. Informers and traitors – men worse than beasts in the field who put their filthy hands on children – hunt them down. Pay them back in the coin of their own crime. Remove them – a match to their thatch. We let them have the lick of sulphur. Lovely word that. Sulphur. Brimstone and sulphur. Some have the knack. Knack to do what? I asked. To keep your mouth shut, he answered. There comes a time for closed lips. I'm tired, love, he said, too tired to tell more. Another day, ask me.

And he has been getting tired. More and more so. Mary's death has taken it out of both of them. I spent most of my time looking after them. Rarely venture out at all, except to give my poor dad a bit of air, for he insists on walking past the house where they live – you know who. He wonders if they're sleeping soundly. And me, I humour him, enjoying the night, because as I say I'm quite a stranger to the city now. Rarely venture out at all. Sophie and Janet, they tried for ages to shake me out of it. Enjoy a night's fun – like the old days – but no go. Kind of them to offer, but it's not me, not any more. I'm not that close to people. As my dad says, best to keep yourself to yourself sometimes. Secrets should stay secrets. Why should the world know your business? That's what I say.

And it's a hard thing to do these days, minding your own business. Everyone seems to be watching everybody else. Cameras everywhere. Mobile phones. Computers. You would think you could get away with nothing, but some people do. It just depends on who you trust. People who know you – people who cover for you – people who lie for you – you have to sniff them out. And if you need to, here's my advice. Don't search too far from your own fireside. Trust your family. You can quote me on that. On all things else though, I stay mum. You can trust me with your life. Though life these days is cheap – life is fleeting, but still and all, my friends, life is full of surprises. Who knows what's coming round the corner?

Our good friends who had nothing to do with Mary's death – Goldilocks and her three bears we've started calling them – they too know how to stick together. These days they're never seen out alone. Safety in numbers. I've never met them. Never set eyes on them. Wouldn't know them from Adam. I'm told the mother is a bit of a bleached blonde. That the lads are strapping men, well built – fit as fiddles. Fine specimens, I'm sure. I'm equally sure there's plenty of good to recommend them. And I know whereof I speak. Didn't I forgive my enemies? Didn't I bless them? And if I know this shower, they are in their way suffering.

She lights a match and lets it fall.

Quite a social life they had, once upon a time, I'm told – all gone, few pubs serve them.

She lights a match and lets it fall.

Quite the ladies' men, the three of them were – not so now, no woman will touch them.

She lights a match and lets it fall.

Just as well they live with their mummy – snug as bugs safe in their little beds.

She lights a match and lets it fall.

I wouldn't know for sure. I know nothing these days except nursing my poor father. He just wants to leave England. Go home to Kerry. To die. We'll go with him. Myself and my mother. It's a full-time job minding him. We barely do anything else – even watch the telly. Who knows what's happening in the outside world? We're quite the hermits. Hear nothing about no one. Still, no news – that's good news, isn't it? And I am all in favour of good news. Good news and good neighbours, that's what we need to survive.

EPISODE TEN

Sal They don't come much better than Sophie, God love her. She's been a rock to us. You could not ask for better. Locked away as we are for most of the time, we depend on that good friend for nearly everything. And she obliges us in all we ask. Once a day she calls – sometimes twice. She even offers to relieve us – go out and enjoy ourselves. But we say no. What if anything should go awry with Dad and us not there? You'd never forgive yourself. And we are quite content, minding him.

His mind, it was starting to go, as fast as his body. He'd start to confuse where he was with where he used to be. One minute he would be clear as daylight talking sensibly. The next he'd suddenly be back in Kerry, crying for his own dead mother. Or he'd think he was back at school, learning the multiplication tables or spelling out hard words, perfectly remembered. My mum might have heard all these stories before, but I loved hearing him repeat them, because I knew this could be the last time I might be listening to his voice. He did get it into his head we would desert him at times, and that did distress him, but we did need to sleep – we couldn't be there twenty-four hours in the day. After our rest he'd interrogate us where we'd been. Having a bit of shut-eye, Dad – upstairs. One night he said he didn't believe us – we'd been out and about – we swore ourselves blue in the face we hadn't put our noses out of the door. He just smiled and said, I told you when to hold your tongue, I'm glad you're learning. Now I think I can go. Hold my hand and we'll wait here safe and sound.

Sophie brought us word about the fire. An inferno, she said. Not that far from here. We know the victims too. It is fair to say we are, in our way, connected. Not by blood – no, more by word of mouth. I didn't quite take it all in. But it seems Goldilocks and the three bears, they've come to a sad end. Not all of them – the mother survived the blaze. One of the sons. Another died running into the blazing building trying to save his brother. People hint he was a kind of pusher – drugged up to the hairy ends of his arse. He likely caused the accident. Cocaine – freebasing – I think that's what Sophie called it. They must all have had a bit of a habit. And it's been getting worse, Sophie said – since, you know, since . . . Did you hear if they cried for mercy? My mother questioned her, did anyone hear them crying? I wouldn't know, Sophie said. I was nowhere near. And neither were we, I said. Nowhere near. I'd best be going, Sophie said. And she was gone. Just like that. We didn't really see her again.

Did see the police though. They called with the news. Mum asked them why they saw fit to bother us with what happened to the strangers. Should they not still be out searching for Mary's killers? Had they forgotten that? Or were they calling to tell us they'd caught the scum of the earth who murdered her granddaughter? Was that why they were here? You'd think that might put a stop to their gallop, but one policeman, he just said, petrol. The fire, it was started by petrol. Two young men are dead – fried alive. Their mother too, she's mourning their lives. So is their brother. They have a right to justice as much as anyone else. And we are going to investigate their murder, for murder it was. They took drugs, didn't they? Mum said. Probably dealt drugs as well. That's why this happened – and you know that. How is their mother? I heard myself asking – I presume her heart is broken. Could you give her a message from me? I know what it's like to lose a kid. She has lost two. She would likely have given her life to save them. Please give my commiserations to the poor woman. Like any parent, I send her my sorrow and sympathy. That's when my dad spoke. He said the word, petrol.

Petrol, yes, the police said. That's what caused the fire. Rough justice, rough justice, my dad kept repeating, rough justice. And you lads need to know who started it? Well, don't waste your time asking us questions. We've been stuck in here. We're each other's witness. I'm nursed every hour of the day by these women. I'm a dying man. With my last breath I swear they are innocent. You come and torment us – you who couldn't catch the filth who killed my granddaughter? Punish us – decent people still pining for their lost child? My poor daughter went public to forgive those killers. The whole world saw and heard her good heart on television. Who would believe otherwise about someone who could be so kind and Christian? Get out of my sight and let me die in peace. Get out – get out.

They went. But as they were going, one stopped. He looked me in the eye. Your old man's Irish, isn't he? Full marks for that deduction, I said. If I were you, the copper said, I'd get back there, you and them. We might believe your dying dad. Others might not. Best if you lie low for a long time. Correction – lie low for life. We do plan on that, I said – go back to Ireland. Thanks for the advice we don't need. We never had much use for you boys in blue. You didn't do me or my daughter much good, did you? I won't hide my face, nor will any belonging to me. And if any try to make us, they will be brought down.

You did it, didn't you? You fucking did it – one of the policewomen said. Her face was the colour of scarlet. You burned two men to death, didn't you? Ask my father – my dying father, I said – I swore I know nothing, and so does he. Do you think he'd sentence himself to hell for telling such a lie? Yes, I do, she said, he will go to hell. That's where he's heading. You would know sweet damn all about hell or heaven, my mother said – when did you last set foot in church or chapel? The next time you do, the policewoman said, get on your knees and never get up again. I saw the state of their charred bodies. Their screams could be heard for miles. They've cursed you for doing this. And they may be heard, their curses, my mother observed calmly, but somehow I doubt that. You were told to get out, I said – what keeps you from going? And with that they turned on their heel and left us.

Music.

Sal We did indeed step inside a church when we took his body back to Kerry, as Dad desired. The clan turned out in strength to give him a great send-off. Mum was in her element, saving the big surprise to be announced after the funeral. We were coming back to Ireland, myself and herself, bag and baggage, to live here among our own. Home are the wanderers, she declared. I don't know what we were expecting when we broke the big story, but the one thing we were certain of was a welcome. And it's fair to say the welcome we received, it was muted. Sure why wouldn't you? – that was the best my Aunt Breda could rise to. A lonely old place, England – it would get to a body. That was the verdict of some cousin or other who'd never set foot outside the country. And as for the rest they just smiled and nodded their heads. It was as if they knew something we didn't, and what they knew they weren't going to tell. The local postman, he made sure we were convinced of that. Half drunk, he let something slip out. Isn't this the safest place you could land yourselves? he said – one thing we hate in this part of the globe, and always have, it's informers. We give them short shift. Your own father lying in the clay, his breed – they knew what to do to any who crossed them or who could not keep their mouth shut. A match to the thatch, he laughed, thinking the rhyme hilarious enough to repeat, a match to the thatch. The same might be applied to yourself, Aunt Breda warned him, if you're heard talking out of order when you're half-cut. Keep your mouth shut, and let that be an end to it.

There never is an end to it, though, is there? No end to grief. Mum didn't long outlast my father. I thought the fresh country air would give her a new lease of life, but it was as if moving took the energy out of her. She started to spend more and more time in bed having the worst of dreams. There was barely a night she didn't wake me with her roars of panic, but she would never tell me what was in them. I did coax her as best as I could, I said spill it all out – maybe then they'll stop tormenting you. But no, I could not get a word out of her. She slept now with photographs of Mary and my dad beside her on the pillow as if they were holy pictures to scare away the devil. I asked her once did she believe in him? Did she believe in hell? She nodded. I said, what does he look like, then, Satan? Can you see him if you believe in him? She said, he's a cross between an old man and a child. His face is wrinkled and wrecked with time, but his voice, it's a young girl's, and it's always wanting something. What is it wanting? I asked her. Revenge, she said. Revenge for being dead, revenge for being born, and that means neither he nor she – the devil and the child – ever will be satisfied. That's when she started to shiver.

Maybe it wasn't a shiver. Maybe it was more of a shake. You wouldn't notice unless you were watching closely. And I did, because face it, in that desolate part of the earth, I hadn't much else to watch. Maybe it was the beginnings of an illness – some palsy or other – but it did not get the chance to develop. Whatever was coming in her dreams, it took her one night, suddenly and silently, in her sleep. She was gone. I'd lost her. Some clean-out, eh? Mother, father, daughter. None left but myself to mourn them. There seemed to be a general consensus on the island I would do a runner quick as she was in the grave back to England. What would a woman my age be doing wasting her life in the back of beyond? What would keep me here but the remnants of my own, and they are dying out, slowly but surely, the relations. All the more reason to remain, I reckoned. Why should I leg it? And no one dared answer me, for there was no possible answer. So I'd like to think – they wanted me to stay put – but bit by bit, it was dawning on me that the whole island, including my people – especially my people – they wanted me out because I felt for some reason they were frightened of me – they believed I was bad luck.

Believe what you want to believe. That's my motto. Live and let live. Let sleeping dogs lie. I sleep easy in my bed. I am where I belong. At peace here, not troubled by the living or the dead. I pine for those that are gone, of course, but that's only human. I wiped my eyes, though, for the last time some while ago. I'm not one who is a professional cry-baby, milking every tragedy for what it can get me. Not like some I can mention. That stupid blonde bitch whose sons came a cropper. I'm told she's still on the warpath blaming all and sundry, not taking responsibility for what they brought on their own heads. You can guess whose loins her darlings sprang from. If I had been their mother, I would have reared them differently. With me they would have learned you have to face the music for what you have done. And I suppose they did learn it.

And here's a funny thing – now I can't listen to music. A long time since I've been able to bear the sound. I can't really say why. It's not that I'm in love with silence or my own voice speaking. It's just that when it starts, the bars of a song, the beat of a drum, even a man in the street whistling – I begin to smell fire or can hear a weapon go off. I keep looking in the music's direction, hoping I'll see Mary dancing up to me, but she's never there. No one is ever there. And the music, it always ends with the blast of the bullet going through her – her blood in the green field, staining the sheep red, roasting them to perfection, the smell of fried meat, and that is my daughter, my dead daughter. The wolves that devoured her, now they are howling, not with pleasure – no, it's with pain and punishment for what they have done, begging – what do they beg for? Mercy and pardon? Forgiveness and blessing they once rejected? Now I reject them, as they are screaming for their mother. Their roaring tongues are silenced by the music of the flames. Did I write that music? Did I start those flames? Does the world know when it looks at me that I am the savage, the mother who took revenge? Does it shake or does it shiver? Am I the palsy? Am I plague? Am I cut from rock to have done what it's said I did? I think that's not quite accurate. I would say instead I am carved from wood. Make that polished wood, for it burns more quickly into dust and nothing.

She smells her hands and holds them out.

I smell of all the coffins I have ever carried. Smell of the bodies I bore to their graves. Smell of the corpse I carried inside me. Daughter, come back to me.

Her hands start to beat against each other.

Come back to me – don't leave me.

Her hands start to tear her flesh.

Mary – come back to me.

Silence.

In the silence she starts to shake, imperceptibly at first, then gathering momentum.

The shaking ceases when she raises her head and howls.

Then she reaches for the match box and strikes a match, letting it fall.

There is now a small mound of burnt matches.

She starts to gather them up in her lap, singing.

Mary had a little lamb
Its fleece was white as snow
Everywhere that Mary went
The lamb was sure to go

It followed her to school one day . . .

Silence.

One morning I sent my daughter out to school before I went to my work. And that day she did not come back. She never came back. And I think I didn't either. Isn't that strange? Here's something stranger. Before this happened, I was like you. Flesh and bone, skin and blood. But now I'm something different. Something neither fish nor fowl. Rock or paper, wood or scissor. I am just a smell. And that smell is sulphur. Touch me, and you burn to death. Come near, I'll destroy you. Because I am what I say I am. The stink – the stench of sulphur. Purest sulphur. Brimstone and sulphur.

She holds up her collection of dead matches, letting one fall as she recites each name.

Father – mother – daughter – friend – foe – sulphur – brimstone and sulphur – father – mother – daughter.